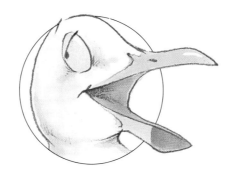

Learn about

OPPOSITES

"Poldy" is a trademark
of World Book, Inc.

World Book, Inc.
525 W. Monroe
Chicago, IL 60661

For information on other
World Book products,
call 1-800-255-1750.

ISBN: 0-7166-6105-5
LC: 95-61310

Printed in Mexico

1 2 3 4 5 6 7 8 9 10 99 98 97 96 95

Learn about
OPPOSITES

World Book, Inc.

a Scott Fetzer company

Chicago   London   Sydney   Toronto

Meet Poldy
and his friends

Poldy the scarecrow was made to scare birds away from a farmer's field. But the birds were not frightened by Poldy. In fact, three birds named Wagtail, Crow, and Seagull became his friends.

When the weather grew cold, Poldy's friends prepared to fly away to wonderful, warm places all over the world. The three birds wanted Poldy to go with them, so they worked together to teach him how to fly. Then Poldy and his friends flew away to see and learn about the world.

In **Learn about Opposites**, Poldy and his friends discover that friendship can make even bad days better.

It was a very bad day for Poldy
and his friends. Things had been
going wrong since morning.

Each time they planned to
do something,

the opposite thing happened.

Poldy wanted to start the
day with a **hot** bath.

But the water was **cold.**

Seagull looked for an
empty branch to sit on.

But every branch was **full.**

Wagtail tried to find a **light** twig.

But all the twigs were too
heavy for him to carry.

Crow hunted for some
sweet berries for lunch.

But he found only **sour** ones.

Poldy wanted a **new** hat.

But he had to wear his **old** one.

Seagull tried to make herself look **fancy.**

But she thought she looked
plain.

Wagtail wanted to cheer everyone up with a **happy** song.

But he could only remember
a **sad** one.

Crow wanted a **quiet**
place to rest.

But every place he went was
noisy.

Poldy should have
turned **left.**

But instead he turned **right.**

Crow wanted **straight** feathers.

But most of his feathers were
crooked.

Wagtail tried to find a
dry place to sit.

But there were **wet**
puddles everywhere.

Crow wanted a **fat** worm
to eat.

But the only worm he found
was **thin.**

Poldy wanted a drink of **clean** water.

But the water in the well was
dirty.

Seagull wanted to be the
first to go to bed.

But she found that she was
the **last.**

"What a day!" Seagull
shrieked. "Today was
like a game of opposites.
Whatever we wanted,
the opposite happened."

"And here's one last opposite to finish the day," said Wagtail. "Even a **bad** day can have a **good** ending!"

Parent notes

Your child probably already understands simple opposites such as *big* and *small, happy* and *sad,* or *hot* and *cold.* These are some of the ideas children use to think about and describe the world around them.

In **Learn about Opposites**, Poldy and his friends are having a bad day. Each time they plan to do something, the opposite happens. Encourage your child to guess what each opposite will be before turning the page to find the answer. Discuss the fact that some words have more than one opposite.

The story includes some concepts that may be new to your child. You can use the questions below to develop your child's understanding of the concepts:

Talking about opposites

Why was it a bad day for Poldy?
Why was it a bad day for Seagull?
Why was it a bad day for Wagtail?
Why was it a bad day for Crow?
Was Poldy's hat new or old?
Did Seagull want to look fancy or plain?
Was Wagtail's song happy or sad?
Did Crow find a quiet place or a noisy one?
Can you think of the opposite of *right*?
Can you think of the opposite of *empty*?
Can you think of the opposite of *dry*?
Can you think of the opposite of *fat*?
Do you have bad days like Poldy and his friends had?

Learning together

Try to provide your child with the opportunity to experience the opposites found in the storybook. For example, when your child has a hot or cold drink, ask him or her to think of a drink that would be the opposite. Encourage your child to make his or her own judgments of happy and sad, or good and bad. Here are more ideas to help you develop your child's understanding of opposites:

Make a scrapbook of opposites. You could have a page of cold things, a page of hot things, a page of hard things, a page of soft things.

Let your child taste some sweet and sour foods. Then make a list of taste opposites.

Play a game with words that have opposites. One of you says a word, and the other gives its opposite.

When you are out walking together, encourage your child to look for opposites. Use a prompt, such as, "I can see something tall. Can you see something short?"

Play a game of *Hunt the Opposites*. Find a big object, a small object, a heavy object, and a light object.